ANDREWS AND McMEEL
A Universal Press Syndicate Company
Kansas City

In memory of my parents, who gave me the gift of imagination.
-BZ

I imagine that this book is dedicated to my family...
both the immediate and the extended variety.
-TB

Special thanks to NEWSDAY, and to managing editor Howard Schneider, for their support and encouragement to create "make beliefs" and to teach students of all ages about our wonderful, amazing world. What other newspaper or editor would have had the imagination or courage to launch such a feature?

ISBN: 0-8362-1048-4

Before You Begin . . .

This is a book to help you imagine and dream—and just have fun. MAKE BELIEFS FOR KIDS encourages you to view your world differently, to see new possibilities, and to make new choices. All you have to do is use your imagination and your heart to respond to this book's questions.

Most of the "make beliefs" you will find here were originally created for NEWSDAY newspaper's nationally syndicated Student Briefing Page. The page teaches students of all ages about current events, and the "make beliefs" were created to encourage readers to express their own views and thoughts about news events and the world in which we live. By writing or drawing their responses to these events, young readers have a more personal stake in the news. And over the years, thousands of completed "make beliefs" were sent to NEWSDAY, which in turn published many of them on the Student Briefing Page.

So now it's your turn to play with "make beliefs." In turning this book's pages, you'll find they constitute a review of some of the key domestic and international issues that were raised over the past few years. Whether tied to the news or not, these "make beliefs" help provide a jumping-off board for you to think about the big issues of our society and our planet—whether they concern the environment, human rights, politics, war, AIDS, science, heroes, or love.

Unlike most books, this one encourages you to ✐ write, ✎ color, and ✏ draw in it; by doing so, you will gain a better sense of who you are and what you stand for. There's even space for you to jot down the date you do so, and each page is perforated for you to ✂ tear out when completed and tape onto your refrigerator or family wall.

MAKE BELIEFS FOR KIDS, with its wonderful drawings, is a magical play book for you, your family, and your friends to explore what is in your heart and imagination. This is a book that only you can complete. You'll probably be surprised at what you learn about yourself.

So enjoy, play, and imagine. Above all, have lots of fun!

Bill Zimmerman

How You Can Use This Book

This fun, interactive book tries to help kids of all ages think about key issues in the world and articulate their thoughts and feelings about them. You'll discover your answers to the questions that follow by listening to your heart and imagination.

This is a book for both children and adults. For those of you who are parents, grandparents, aunts and uncles, or big brothers and sisters, why not sit down with the children in your life one evening after work or weekend morning and do a "make belief" together? Each of you can take turns writing and coloring.

Playing "make beliefs" with another person will give you a unique insight into how your minds and spirits work. If your child is too young to read the questions, you can read them aloud, think together about possible answers, and then ask the child to color in or dictate a response that you can write for her or him. This will reinforce the value of a young person's creative voice.

Over the years I've received letters from a wide range of users of "make beliefs": from teachers and children in elementary schools; to teenagers and college students; to parents looking for a way to play with their children; to business executives seeking a resource to help them calm down and tap into their creativity; to senior citizens who want to help in recapturing their imaginations.

Our best parents and educators understand that playing is learning. Many graduate schools use "make beliefs" to teach new teachers how to spur creativity and imagination in the classroom. In turn, educators use such "make beliefs" to encourage youngsters to practice language, reading, and creative thinking skills. Many teachers also use the individual "make beliefs" as subjects for essays, poems, and plays. One very imaginative musician, who teaches opera writing, has his students sing their responses to the "make beliefs." You can even use this book at a party and encourage your guests to take turns writing their responses to one of the pages.

Completing a "make belief" encourages people to think deeply about the world, to hear their inner voice, and even to try to see the world through a different point of view.

Many activity directors at social agencies that work with abused or disabled children, or with adults who have special needs, or with elderly, withdrawn people, can use this book's magical, whimsical drawings and suppositions as a way to draw others out of their silences and give voice to their feelings. And as people write down responses to the "make beliefs," they often get a better understanding of their own beliefs and values.

For those, too, who teach young and old how to read and learn English as a second language, MAKE BELIEFS FOR KIDS is an invaluable, nonthreatening tool for helping people try their new language skills. You'll also find that the book's drawings depict a diverse universe of people of all colors and cultures. Not all people look the same, and a book should reflect the richness of different people in our world.

Whether you complete this book on your own or use it to play with someone else, please try to remember one simple rule: there is no single "right" answer to each "make belief"; the only true answer is the one that comes straight from your heart.

SHARE WITH US

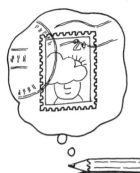

Dear reader,

Please share with us your own "make beliefs" that spring from your imagination. Perhaps we can incorporate some of them in future editions. We also welcome your comments and suggestions on MAKE BELIEFS FOR KIDS. Is there any way we can make this book more useful or pleasurable to you?

Please write to:

Bill Zimmerman
Guarionex Press
201 West 77 Street
New York, NY 10024

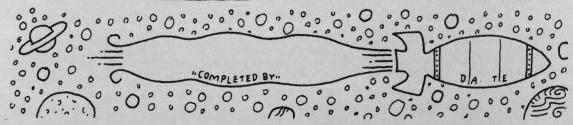

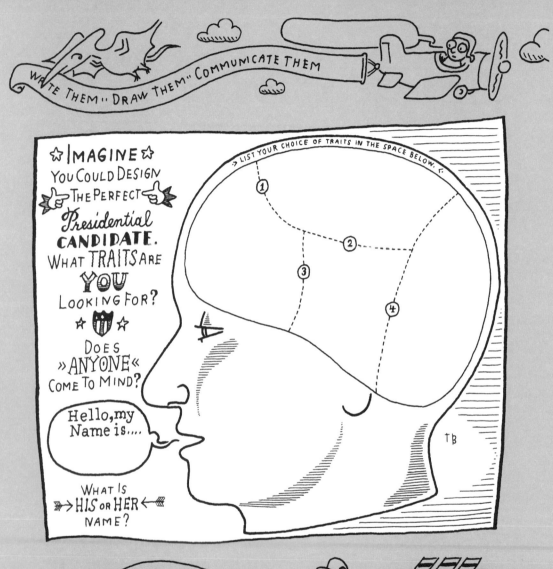

IMAGINE YOU COULD COMPETE IN THE OLYMPICS AND DEMONSTRATE A SPECIAL TALENT — PHYSICAL OR INTELLECTUAL. IN WHAT EVENT WOULD YOU HOPE TO BRING HOME THE GOLD?

→ WHO WOULD BE ON *YOUR* DREAM TEAM? – – – – – – – – – – – – –

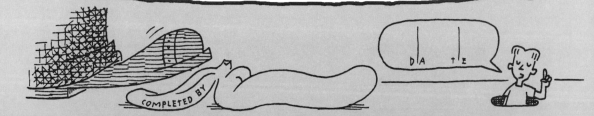

IMAGINE BY WISHING ON A STAR YOUR DEEPEST HOPE WOULD COME TRUE FOR THE NEW YEAR, WHAT IS IT?

>> CONNECT THE STARS AND SEE OUR WISH FOR YOU <<

"COMPLETED BY

DATE

WRITE THEM. DRAW THEM. ENJOY THEM

IMAGINE LIKE DOCTOR FRANKENSTEIN YOU COULD CREATE A NEW HUMAN BEING FROM THE PARTS OF OTHERS. WHAT TYPE OF CREATURE WOULD YOU CREATE?

THE HEART OF.. THE EYES OF.. THE LAUGHTER OF.. THE SOUL OF.. TH..

FILL IN NAME

>>DESCRIBE YOUR CREATION..

>> I'D CALL THE CREATURE..

THE BODY OF..

IMAGINE, LIKE FRANKENSTEIN AUTHORESS MARY SHELLEY, YOU WROTE A SUPERNATURAL TALE "TO CURDLE THE BLOOD, AND QUICKEN THE BEATINGS OF THE HEART." WHAT WOULD BE THE OPENING LINES OF YOUR GHOST STORY? WHAT WOULD ITS TITLE BE?

~ OPENING LINES ~

"COMPLETED BY"

DATE

WRITE THEM · DRAW THEM · PRINT THEM

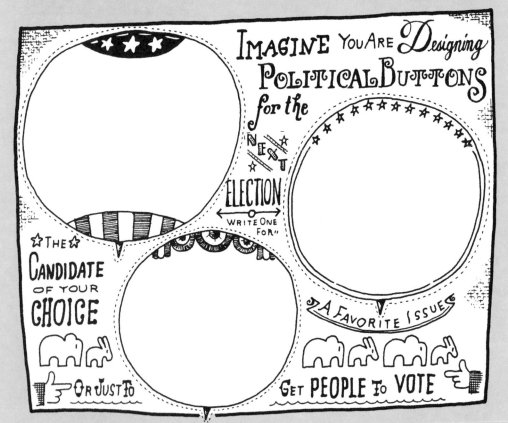

IMAGINE YOU ARE Designing POLITICAL BUTTONS for the NEXT ELECTION

WRITE ONE FOR"

☆ THE ☆ CANDIDATE OF YOUR CHOICE

A FAVORITE ISSUE

Or Just To

GET PEOPLE To VOTE

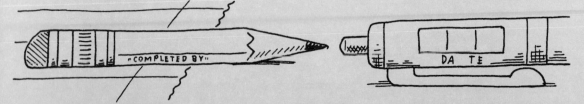

"COMPLETED BY"

DATE

THINK IT UP   PUT IT DOWN   SEND IT OFF   BOING

IMAGINE THAT, LIKE THE POET WALT WHITMAN, (THAT'S ME) YOU ARE WRITING A POEM, A RHYME, A SONG OF YOUR SELF, WHAT WOULD YOU WRITE? WHAT SONG WOULD YOU SING?

» Song Of Myself «
AS WRITTEN BY

"YOUR NAME GOES HERE PLEASE"

COMPLETED BY..

DA TE

WRITE THEM" DRAW THEM" SURPRISE THEM

IMAGINE YOU WERE DESIGNING A PANEL TO ADD TO

THE NATIONAL AIDS QUILT

THE NAMES PROJECT

TO HELP REMEMBER PEOPLE WHO HAVE DIED OF THIS DISEASE, WHAT WOULD YOUR PANEL LOOK LIKE?

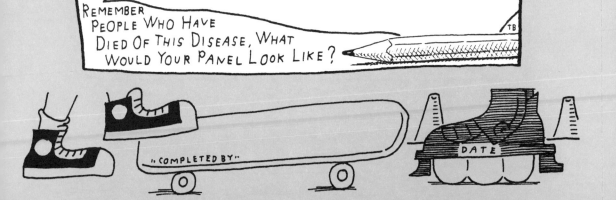

"COMPLETED BY"

DATE

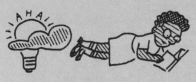

WRITE THEM · DRAW THEM · DELIVER THEM

IMAGINE, FOR VALENTINE'S DAY, YOU COULD WRITE A GREETING TO ANY PUBLIC FIGURE. TO WHOM WOULD YOU SEND IT, AND WHAT WOULD IT SAY?

"COMPLETED BY

DATE

IMAGINE THAT UNDER THE U.S./SOVIET ARMS TREATY, EVERY NUCLEAR WARHEAD COULD BE RESET TO DELIVER A MESSAGE OF PEACE INSTEAD OF DESTRUCTION, WHAT WOULD YOUR WRITTEN » MISSILE « SAY, AND TO WHOM WOULD YOU SEND IT?

R.I.P.

"To"
"Message"

"COMPLETED BY"

"DATE"

"WRITE THEM" "DRAW THEM"
CELEBRATE THEM

IMAGINE YOU COULD PRODUCE THE PERFECT SUMMER MOVIE. WHAT WOULD IT BE ABOUT, AND WHO WOULD STAR IN IT?

GIVE THE MOVIE A TITLE »

"COMPLETED BY"

DATE

IMAGINE YOU FOUND THE WINNING TICKET TO THE STATE LOTTERY. IF YOU SPENT THAT MONEY TO IMPROVE THE AILING SCHOOL SYSTEM, HOW WOULD YOU PUT THESE FUNDS TO USE?

"COMPLETED BY"

DATE

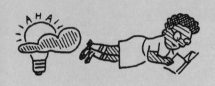

WRITE THEM · DRAW THEM · PRODUCE THEM

IMAGINE YOU ASKED CONGRESS FOR $11 BILLION TO FUND A SCIENCE PROJECT TO BETTER UNDERSTAND OUR UNIVERSE. WHAT WOULD BE YOUR GOAL?

"COMPLETED BY" DATE

IMAGINE THAT YOU WENT TO CHINA AS A DELEGATE TO THE UN WORLD CONFERENCE ON WOMEN. WHAT IDEAS WOULD YOU BRING UP TO ADVANCE THE RIGHTS OF WOMEN AND TO HELP END DISCRIMINATION AND VIOLENCE AGAINST THEM THROUGHOUT THE WORLD?

"COMPLETED BY"

DATE

"WRITE THEM" "DRAW THEM" "SING THEM"

IMAGINE YOU WERE HELD HOSTAGE, LIKE NEWSMAN TERRY ANDERSON

ONCE WAS IN LEBANON, AND TO KEEP UP YOUR SPIRITS, YOU WROTE POETRY. WHAT POEMS WOULD YOU WRITE IF YOU HAD BEEN IN HIS PLACE?

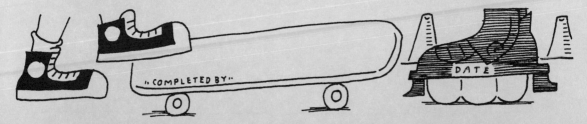

"COMPLETED BY"

DATE

IMAGINE You Could Look Into Your Crystal Ball And Predict The Top Three News Events Or Newsmakers Of This Year. What Do You See? What Is Your Greatest Hope For The Nation For The New Year?

"COMPLETED BY"

DATE

IMAGINE THAT THE FREEDOM TO READ ANY BOOK YOU WANTED WAS TAKEN AWAY. WHAT WOULD LIFE BE LIKE IN A WORLD LIKE THAT?

>> HOW WOULD THAT LOSS CHANGE YOUR LIFE? <<

.. COMPLETED BY ..

DATE

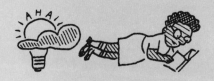

IMAGINE THAT YOU COULD READ THE MINDS OF THOSE INVOLVED IN HELPING TO ESTABLISH PEACE IN BOSNIA. WHAT ARE THEIR THOUGHTS?

THE PRESIDENT (BILL CLINTON)

THE MILITARY (U.S. TROOPS)

THE CITIZENRY (YOU)

"COMPLETED BY"

DATE

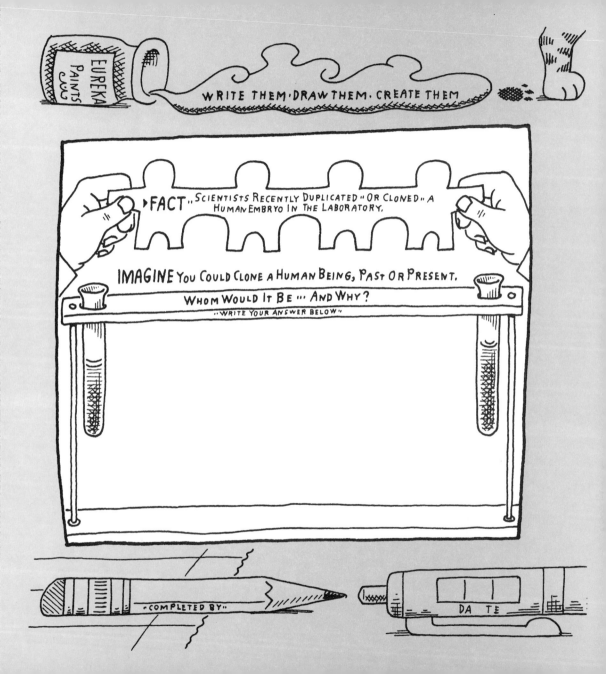

WRITE THEM · DRAW THEM · CREATE THEM

EUREKA PAINTS

▸FACT,, SCIENTISTS RECENTLY DUPLICATED "OR CLONED" A HUMAN EMBRYO IN THE LABORATORY.

IMAGINE YOU COULD CLONE A HUMAN BEING, PAST OR PRESENT.

WHOM WOULD IT BE ··· AND WHY?

,,WRITE YOUR ANSWER BELOW"

"COMPLETED BY"

DATE

THINK IT UP PUT IT DOWN SEND IT OFF

IMAGINE YOU ARE THE HEAD OF A TV NETWORK..... AND WANT TO

CREATE A NEW SERIES FOR KIDS THAT IS FUN BUT **NOT VIOLENT**

WHAT WILL IT BE ABOUT? WHAT WOULD YOU CALL IT?

BOING

COMPLETED BY...

DATE

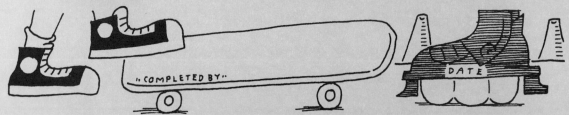

IMAGINE YOU COULD GIVE A PARTY AND INVITE CHARACTERS FROM YOUR FAVORITE BOOKS. WHOM WOULD YOU LIKE TO INVITE?

IT'S A PARTY!

"COMPLETED BY"

IMAGINE YOU WROTE THE STATE OF THE UNION SPEECH THAT PRESIDENT CLINTON READ FROM THE TELEPROMPTER TO THE AMERICAN PEOPLE. WHAT WOULD YOU HAVE WRITTEN?

.. COMPLETED BY..

DATE

IMAGINE THAT YOU WERE HELPING TO CREATE A NEW INTERNATIONAL GROUP THAT WAS DEDICATED TO THE TASK OF PRESERVING PEACE AMONG NATIONS AND ALSO MAKING THE WORLD A BETTER, SAFER PLACE TO LIVE FOR THE NEXT FIFTY YEARS. WHAT WOULD YOU LIKE TO CALL YOUR ORGANIZATION?

WHAT WOULD YOUR CHARTER CALL FOR?

IMAGINE A WORLD WITHOUT A UNITED NATIONS. HOW WOULD THAT BE?

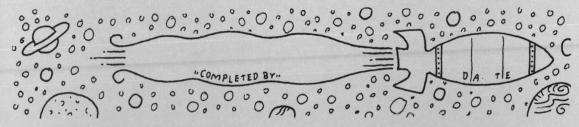

"COMPLETED BY"

DATE

IMAGINE CONDITIONS WERE SO BAD THAT YOU WERE FORCED TO FLEE YOUR HOMELAND, LEAVING BEHIND THE PEOPLE AND THINGS YOU LOVE. AS A REFUGEE WHERE WOULD YOU GO? WHAT WOULD YOUR GREATEST HOPE AND WISH BE?

COMPLETED BY

DATE

WRITE THEM · DRAW THEM · INSPIRE THEM

EUREKA PAINTS

IMAGINE YOU COULD FILM A FAVORITE BOOK. WHICH ONE WOULD IT BE? WHOM WOULD YOU CAST IN THE PARTS?

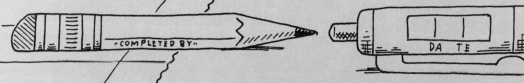

"COMPLETED BY"

DATE

IMAGINE

WE COULD ELIMINATE POVERTY, PROVIDE FOR ALL OUR NEEDY, EMPLOY ALL ABLE-BODIED PEOPLE, AND CARE FOR OUR SICK AND ELDERLY. HOW DO WE DO THIS? HOW WOULD THE NATION BENEFIT?

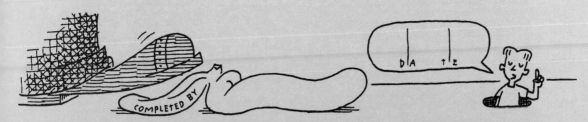

COMPLETED BY

DATE

"WRITE THEM" "DRAW THEM"
"DISCUSS THEM

WRITE ABOUT YOUR SELECTION HERE "OR IF YOU PREFER PASTE IN A PICTURE TOO.

IMAGINE YOU HAD THE POWER TO SAVE ANY ONE OF THE WORLD'S ENDANGERED ANIMALS OR PLANTS, WHICH ONE WOULD YOU HELP, AND WHY?

"COMPLETED BY"

DATE

IMAGINE A WORLD IN WHICH EVERYONE HAD A GUN, WHAT WOULD LIFE BE LIKE? HOW WOULD THE COURSE OF HISTORY BE DIFFERENT?

In Which World Would You FEEL SAFER? (CHOOSE ONE)

IMAGINE A WORLD WITHOUT GUNS, WHAT WOULD LIFE BE LIKE? HOW WOULD THE COURSE OF HISTORY BE DIFFERENT?

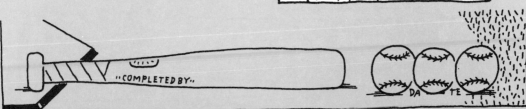

"COMPLETED BY"

DATE

IMAGINE YOU ARE CREATING THE FIRST U.S. CENSUS OF STUDENTS.

WHAT KEY QUESTIONS WOULD YOU ASK PEOPLE YOUR AGE?

.. COMPLETED BY..

DATE

IMAGINE THAT YOU HAVE JUST BEEN SWORN IN AS OUR PRESIDENT. HOW WILL YOU CHANGE THINGS IN OUR COUNTRY?

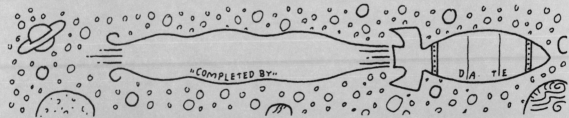

"COMPLETED BY"

DATE

IMAGINE THAT YOU WERE OUR NATION'S POET LAUREATE PENNING A POEM ABOUT SOMETHING·· OR SOMEONE··VERY MEANINGFUL TO YOU. WHAT WOULD YOUR OPENING LINES BE?

"COMPLETED BY

DATE

IMAGINE YOU WERE HELPING DAVID LETTERMAN COMPILE THE »TOP 10 LIST« OF GOOFY, WACKY THINGS TO DO THIS SUMMER. WHAT WOULD YOU LIST?

1.
2.
3.
4.
5.
6.
7.
8.
9.
10.

WRITE THEM "DRAW THEM" DISPLAY THEM

"COMPLETED BY"

DATE

IMAGINE THAT YOU AND YOUR FAMILY SUDDENLY BECAME HOMELESS DUE TO A CATASTROPHE— SUCH AS AN EARTHQUAKE, A FIRE, LOSS OF A JOB, A FLOOD, OR EVICTION. WHAT THINGS WOULD YOU DO TO HELP KEEP YOUR FAMILY TOGETHER?

WHAT WOULD YOU DO TO HELP A HOMELESS FAMILY?

COMPLETED BY:

DATE

IMAGINE YOU COULD NOMINATE SOMEONE YOU KNOW TO BE ONE OF THE PRESIDENT'S »FACES OF HOPE« ''' A PERSON WHO SHOWS »INCREDIBLE COURAGE« AND MAKES A DIFFERENCE, WHOM WOULD YOU CHOOSE AND WHY?

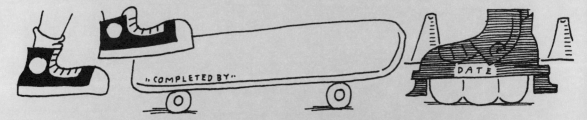

"COMPLETED BY"

DATE

YO! TEEN READERS, IMAGINE YOU'RE THE EDITOR OF A NEWSPAPER. COOL, HUH? WHAT FEATURES, TOPICS WOULD YOU ADD OR CHANGE TO MAKE IT MORE APPEALING, AND A HAPPENING KIND OF PUBLICATION FOR PEOPLE YOUR AGE?

"COMPLETED BY"

DATE

IMAGINE YOU COULD INCLUDE A MESSAGE WITH THE FOOD AND RELIEF SUPPLIES THAT THE UNITED STATES DROPS OVER BOSNIA-HERZEGOVINA TO HELP THE PEOPLE THERE. WHAT WOULD YOU SAY TO THEM?

WAY TO GO!

FILL IN TEAR OUT HANG UP

"COMPLETED BY"

DATE

WRITE THEM · DRAW THEM · PRODUCE THEM

EUREKA PAINTS

ON THIS THANKSGIVING,

IMAGINE A DAY WITHOUT TEARS OR GRIEF, A DAY WITHOUT SHOOTINGS AND CRIME, A DAY WITHOUT DRUGS, A DAY WITHOUT HUNGER...., WHAT STORIES WOULD BE TOLD?

WHAT ARE YOU THANKFUL FOR?

"COMPLETED BY"

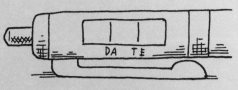

DATE

IMAGINE You Could Change The Ending Of A Book. What Book Would You Choose? What Would Your New Ending Be?

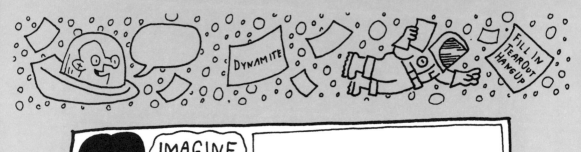

IMAGINE

THAT YOU PUT A GREAT LITTLE BAND TOGETHER WHICH WOULD INFLUENCE POPULAR MUSIC AND CULTURE AS MUCH AS THE BEATLES DID. WHAT WOULD YOU CALL YOUR GROUP? NAME THE FIRST SINGLE, THEN DESIGN THE CD ART, WRITE A BRIEF DESCRIPTION OF THE MUSIC.

>> THE COVER << DESIGN IT <<

"TITLE"

"GROUP"

>> THE SINGLE " NAME IT <<

>> THE REVIEW "WRITE IT <<

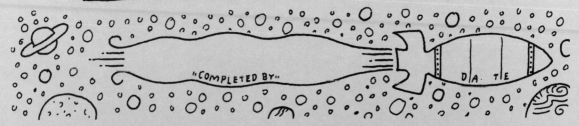

"COMPLETED BY"

DATE

IMAGINE YOU ARE DESIGNING A POSTER THAT TAKES A STAND EITHER FOR OR AGAINST LAWS TO CONTROL THE SALE OF HANDGUNS. WHAT WOULD IT SAY OR LOOK LIKE?

COMPLETED BY

DATE

WRITE THEM "DRAW THEM" SAVE THEM

IMAGINE THAT DURING THE NEW SCHOOL YEAR YOU WILL BE ABLE TO ACHIEVE A GOAL YOU'VE ALWAYS HAD, WHAT WOULD IT BE?

"COMPLETED BY" DATE

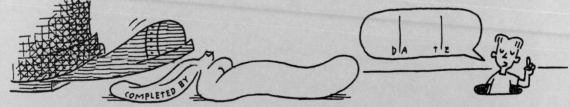

MAKE BELIEVE YOU CAN MAKE YOUR DREAMS COME TRUE.

BILL ZIMMERMAN, the creator of MAKE BELIEFS FOR KIDS, has been a dreamer and a questioner all his life. A journalist for more than twenty years and a prize-winning editor, Zimmerman is editor of the nationally syndicated Student Briefing Page for NEWSDAY, one of the nation's largest newspapers. His other books are DOGMAS: SIMPLE TRUTHS FROM A WISE PET; THE LITTLE BOOK OF JOY: AN INTERACTIVE JOURNAL FOR THOUGHTS, PRAYERS, AND WISHES; HOW TO TAPE INSTANT ORAL BIOGRAPHIES, a book that teaches you how to capture your family stories on audio and video tape; LIFELINES: A BOOK OF HOPE, which offers comforting thoughts; and A BOOK OF QUESTIONS TO KEEP THOUGHTS AND FEELINGS, a new form of diary/journal.

TOM BLOOM has drawn inspiration from his dreams for a number of years and is usually dreaming even as he draws. His work appears in the NEW YORK TIMES, NEWSDAY, BARRON'S, GAMES, the NEW YORKER, and others as you may well imagine, and while he does not pretend to live in a land of make believe, you can often find him on cloud nine.